Brain Teasers

FOR

DUMMIES®

POCKET EDITION

Brain Teasers
FOR
DUMMIES®
POCKET EDITION

by Timothy E. Parker

WILEY

Wiley Publishing, Inc.

Brain Teasers For Dummies, Pocket Edition

Published by
Wiley Publishing, Inc.
111 River Street
Hoboken, NJ 07030-5774
www.wiley.com

Table of Contents

Introduction

Sure, puzzles are fun. They're a great diversion when you're sitting on a plane or getting sneezed on in the waiting room at the doctor's office. And if enjoyment is your one and only reason for picking up this book, you'll get no argument from me. (After all, I enjoy a good puzzle myself!)

But here's the great news: This kind of fun is actually good for you. Specifically, it's good for your brain. So welcome to the mental gym, where the equipment is portable, your exercise area is private, and the after-workout shower is completely optional.

About This Book

I bet that when you were a kid, you didn't schedule physical exercise into your day. You kept your body strong by doing what felt natural: riding your bike, skipping rope, climbing trees. . . . But these days, to stay in shape, chances are you're much more deliberate. You probably don't climb trees the way you used to, so you have to actively seek out exercise or accept that you'll be a little weaker and slower with each passing year.

Countless articles, books, and Web sites are now devoted to the idea that if you don't want to lose it ("it" being your mental sharpness), you'd better use it ("it" being your brain). And sure, you could give your gray matter a decent workout by dusting off that anthology of 19th-century literature that's been sitting on your shelf since college, but doesn't a puzzle sound more fun?

That's why I created this book: to give your brain a challenge you'll really enjoy, so you can get on the path to greater mental fitness and truly enjoy the workout.

Conventions Used in This Book

Before I get to the meat of this book — the puzzles themselves — I spend some time touting the benefits of mental exercise in Chapter 1. In this chapter, I include a handful of Web site addresses so you can explore additional resources if you'd like. The Web addresses appear in monofont, which makes them easier to locate if you want to go back and find them after you're done reading.

How This Book Is Organized

The bulk of this book is devoted to what you came looking for: puzzles (and their answers). But in case one or more of these puzzle types are new to you, I first spend some time explaining each and suggesting some strategies for working them.

Chapter 1: Preparing Your Puzzle Strategies

My first task in this part is to introduce you to the reasons for spending some quality time with this book. I explore what recent research says about the importance of mental exercise and the impact it can have on your cognitive abilities — including your memory — as you age.

I then introduce each type of puzzle that appears in this book and provide tips for solving it. From crosswords and word games to Sudoku and logic puzzles, I help you prepare for the workout that's coming.

Chapter 2: Getting a Puzzle Workout

Here's what you've been waiting for: the puzzles themselves. The logic puzzles come first, followed by riddles, cryptograms, word scrambles, word searches, crosswords, and Sudoku puzzles.

For each type of puzzle, I offer various levels of difficulty; the easier puzzles come first, followed by fairly tough puzzles, and then by downright treacherous ones — the kind that will keep you awake until the wee hours, cursing my name!

Chapter 3: Checking Your Answers

Pretty please, no matter how much you're tempted, don't look at this chapter until you've spent some quality time with Chapter 2. Think of it as exercising your willpower at the same time you're pumping those brain cells.

Icons Used in This Book

In Chapter 1, you'll notice two icons in the margins that help you navigate the text:

When you see this icon, know that the text next to it contains a helpful hint for solving puzzles.

This icon points out information that you want to tuck into your mental filing cabinet — it's worth holding on to.

Where to Go from Here

You've got your minibook copy of *Brain Teasers For Dummies, Pocket Edition* — now what? Chapter 1 of this minibook gives you the basic rules for each type of puzzle included as well as some solving tips. If you're ready to start solving puzzles, head straight to Chapter 2. The answers are in Chapter 3. If you want even more strategies on solving crosswords, word games, and logic puzzles or if you've solved all the puzzles in this minibook and are itching for more, check out the full-size version of *Brain Games For Dummies* — simply head to your local book seller or go to www.dummies.com!

Chapter 1

Preparing Your Puzzle Strategies

· ·

In This Part

▶ Taking a peek inside your brain

▶ Storing up ammunition against Alzheimer's

▶ Getting your body and mind in tip-top shape

▶ Choosing your puzzle poison

· ·

*B*e honest: Do you feel as mentally sharp today as you did when you were 20? (If you're 20 now, or even younger, indulge me for a moment while I address your elders.) Can you retain information as easily as you did at that age? Or do you suspect that you don't learn as quickly as you once did, and worry about occasional fuzzy moments when you can't recall things that used to be second-nature?

If you're in the "fuzzy" category, even on rare occasions, you may feel a bit anxious about the changes that seem to be taking place in your brain. And you may wonder what, if anything, you can do about them. I suspect that may be why you're reading this part right now, as opposed to jumping straight into Chapter 2 of this book and trying your hand at the puzzle of your choice.

As an isolated activity, working a crossword puzzle or untangling a word scramble may not dramatically change anyone's cognitive ability. But combined with other lifestyle changes, working puzzles — or doing other types of mentally stimulating activities — may have profound long-term effects on memory and overall cognitive ability. That's why I devote this first part to the big picture of working puzzles: why they're potentially beneficial, and what else you can do to try to recapture your 20s (if only in your mind!).

Pumping Up Your Synapses

You may suspect that *I'm* the one who needs some mental help, writing about synapses in a puzzle book. But bear with me — I'll try to demonstrate that I haven't gone around the bend.

On the off chance you aren't a neurologist, let me start with a couple definitions. *Neurons* are cells that control your central nervous system: your brain and spinal column, and the nerves connected to them. *Synapses* are tiny gaps between the neurons in your brain. When synapses are working correctly, they allow your neurons to communicate with each other, which keeps your nervous system functioning the way it should.

Your nervous system must function properly in order for you to learn new things, retain information, and use your powers of logic and reason.

You're feeling some love for your synapses now, aren't you?

You have about 100 billion neurons in your brain. And you have literally trillions of synapses — possibly even a *quadrillion* (that's a 1 followed by 15 zeroes). It sure seems like you have plenty to spare, but as you age, your synapses deteriorate. And because your brain activity takes place courtesy of synapses, their deterioration equates to a decrease in your brain function, including memory.

The take-home lesson here is that if you want your mind to live to a ripe old age, you need to do more than just take care of your body (although that's crucial too, as I explain later in this chapter). You need to keep your synapses in top condition. How do you do that? Keep reading!

Building a Cognitive Reserve

Obviously, no one is offering guarantees here. I can't promise that anything I suggest in this book will add X number of years to your life, and that those years will be free of any symptoms of memory loss or other mental decline. But study after study in the past two decades has shown that mental activity can — and often does — have a positive effect on your quality of life in the long run, and I can't argue with that.

How do you build a cognitive reserve? The same way that you keep your synapses happy and healthy. Keep reading — the following section offers specific suggestions.

The key to a strong cognitive reserve seems to be to start as early as you can. The younger you are when you begin actively pursuing brain fitness, the greater the reserve you can accumulate. But if you're already past "early," don't panic — just make the commitment to start now. Some studies have shown that even people well into their 70s can improve their cognitive health by making lifestyle changes and increasing their mental stimulation.

Taking a Whole-Body Approach to Brain Health

The great news about the steps you can take to improve your chances of long-term cognitive health is that many of them are the same steps you take to keep your body healthy. You need to add just a couple items to a list that's probably already familiar. And the new items are fun — promise.

Here's the familiar stuff:

✔ **Reduce stress.** If you've heard this advice from your doctor in relation to a physical condition, you now have double the reason to heed it. Research shows that stress causes synapses to malfunction.

Long-term stress can cause a *neurotransmitter* (a chemical that carries messages between nerve cells) called glutamate to build up in your synapses. If enough of it accumulates, it can become toxic and interfere with your memory and your ability to learn.

✔ **Get aerobic exercise.** Aerobic exercise can help you manage and resist stress, which is enough reason to make it part of your daily routine. But among its many other benefits, studies suggest that it stimulates the creation of new neurons and strengthens the connections between them.

✔ **Eat a diet rich in antioxidant foods.** If your physical health alone hasn't inspired you to stock up on blueberries and spinach, do so for your mental health. Foods rich in antioxidants may help counteract effects of free radicals in your brain. (*Free radicals* are molecules that contain oxygen that attack cells throughout your body. They have been linked to cancer and heart disease, as well as brain deterioration.)

✔ **Control high blood pressure and diabetes.** A study published in the journal *Neurology* in 2001 showed that the mental abilities of participants with high blood pressure or diabetes declined more rapidly than those of other participants. High blood pressure is a risk factor for a condition called *vascular dementia,* in which a series of tiny strokes can affect memory and other cognitive abilities.

Ready for the steps that may be new on your to-do list?

✔ **Get lots of mental stimulation.** Ahhh, *this* is where the puzzles come in — finally!

You may be hard-pressed to find a scientist who would claim to know exactly how much mental stimulation the average adult of a certain age needs, or what types of mental activities are best for a certain population. The science is fairly young, and I guarantee you'll hear a lot more about it in the years to come. But the general consensus is this: Mental stimulation of any kind can have positive effects on warding off memory problems and other declines in cognitive function. And lack of stimulation is a serious factor in mental decline.

So, how should you use your brain to get the maximum results? Only you can answer that question. That's because whatever you do, it has to be enjoyable enough to truly stimulate you and to keep you coming back for more, day after day. We're talking about running a mental marathon here — not winning a sprint. So you have my permission to read *War and Peace* or pull out your old calculus textbook, but only if that's what you really *want*. Otherwise, I suggest you look for other types of activities that will keep you interested in the long term. (Anyone for sudoku?)

The bottom line: If there's a hobby you love that you haven't made time for in years, make time for it. If there's an activity you've been meaning to do but have put on the back burner because it seems less important than folding laundry, do it. If there's a subject you've been curious about for ages but haven't had time to study, study it. And if anyone (including your conscience) pesters you about how you're spending your time, memorize your new mantra: *My brain needs me.*

✔ **Stay curious.** This is an extension of the previous point. If you've buried your curiosity about the world around you because you haven't had time to explore it since childhood, now's the time — no matter how old you are or what your life circumstances are — to rediscover how curiosity feels.

Toss out the mindset that you learned everything you need to know years ago, and you can rest on your laurels for the rest of your life. We live in a fascinating, quick-changing world, and I *promise* you'll never run out of new things to discover.

Finding Out More About Cognitive Fitness

The connection between mental stimulation and cognitive fitness has received a lot of attention in the past two decades, and it's bound to be the focus of many more studies, articles, books, Web sites, and software programs in the years to come. This part barely scratches the surface of the subject, and I encourage you to find out more (especially if you're truly curious about it, because what better way to stimulate your brain than to read about stimulating your brain?).

Following are just a handful of resources to consider:

- ✔ **Alzheimer's Association:** From the home page (www.alz.org), you can find a wealth of information on the disease. If you click on the "We Can Help" tab and go to "Brain Health," you'll find helpful links, including to a crossword puzzle site!

- ✔ **American Association of Retired People (AARP):** The Web site www.aarp.org/health/brain features links to articles on the latest brain research, tips for keeping your brain healthy, and information about the Staying Sharp initiative.

- ✔ **Brain Fitness Channel:** At http://bfc.posit science.com, you can test your current level of brain fitness, read news stories about brain research, study how the brain functions, take part in online forums that focus on specific subjects that may interest you, and more.

- ✔ **Prevention:** The magazine's Web site (www.prevention.com) features a Brain Fitness section that you access through the "Health" tab on the home page. You'll find lots of articles that link physical and mental fitness, and you can join the Prevention online community to share stories or ask for feedback from other people with similar interests and concerns.

- ✔ **SharpBrains:** The home page of www.sharp brains.com provides links to more information than any one brain may be able to absorb. Whether you want to read about brain training software, nutrition, memory, stress management, or just about anything else brain-related, you have a good chance of finding what you're looking for here.

Picking the Type of Puzzle That Suits You

To get your mental fitness plan off to a great start, I offer puzzle options in Chapter 2 of this book. Which type should you tackle first? Only you can answer that question, but in this section, I offer a brief overview of each so you can consider what interests you most.

Logic puzzles and riddles

If you want to test your logic but prefer to work with words instead of numbers, you may find that logic puzzles and riddles are your best bet. These types of puzzles are comforting in their familiarity — most of us have been solving them since we were kids. But that doesn't mean they're easy to solve; they can definitely help keep your mind sharp.

The great fun of logic puzzles and riddles is that you realize the puzzle constructor is trying to trick you. You're essentially matching wits, one-on-one, with the person who wrote the puzzle or riddle. And often, the answers are simple, if you can weed out the deceptive language or images hiding the solutions.

If you're afraid solving logic puzzles and riddles will make you feel like you're taking a college entrance exam, I encourage you to try out the ones in Chapter 2. I suspect you *will* feel like a kid again, but only in the best way.

When you tackle logic puzzles or riddles, you're pitting your wits against those of the puzzle constructor. Keep the following in mind.

- ✔ Each puzzle or riddle should have just one answer. If you can think of more than one answer that makes good sense, chances are you've out-witted the puzzle constructor!

- ✔ The language of the puzzle or riddle may be designed to veil the answer — to deceive and distract you. That's not always the case, but when it is, your job is to study the language and figure out what's being hidden. Sometimes a single word can crack open the solution.

> ✔ If you're stumped, you're better off stepping away
> than turning to the answer page. Come back to
> the puzzle or riddle later with a fresh perspective,
> and the answer may jump out.

Word games

I include three types of word games in this book: word searches, scrambles, and cryptograms. Of the three, I find word searches the least taxing and most relaxing. On days when you just aren't quite up to the challenge of, for example, a crossword, a word search may fit the bill. If you're willing to be methodical (by reading each letter in each row or column), you can locate every word on the list provided by the puzzle constructor. You get the relaxation that comes with focusing on a finite task, plus the satisfaction of success when you check off the final word.

Word scrambles usually don't require a big time commitment and can be a great choice when time is limited. Some of the scrambles in this book are only five letters long, for example — you can work several of them in a matter of minutes. And when you have more than a few minutes available, the more complicated scrambles are fun to tackle. You may get stuck on some of them, but usually if you just keep scribbling possible combinations, you'll have an "aha!" moment — the best kind of moment a puzzler can experience.

If you have the mind of a detective (and watch way too many hours of *CSI* and its various derivatives), cryptograms may be your puzzle of choice. In this type of puzzle, a phrase or sentence is *encrypted* — each letter is substituted with a different letter or character. For example, every "e" may be replaced with an "h" and every "t" replaced with a "g." To figure out what the sentence or phrase says, you have to figure out each substitution. Even the easiest cryptograms aren't necessarily easy when compared to a word search, for example. But if you like a good mystery and want the extra mental workout that comes with the challenge, these puzzles may be exactly what you need.

If your puzzle of choice is a word search, word scramble, or cryptogram, keep the following tips in mind.

- ✔ When you work a word search, being methodical is your best bet. Use a straight edge to guide your eyes if necessary, and check each row or column for the first letter of the word you're looking for.

- ✔ If you get stuck on a word scramble, write the letters in as many different orders as possible until something looks familiar. If you're looking at lots of letters, try to find common groupings such as *sh, th,* or *ing.*

- ✔ When working a cryptogram, pay close attention to any hints provided. Look at one-, two-, and three-letter words first, and always use a pencil — you're likely going to make some guesses before arriving at the solution.

Crosswords

The concept of the crossword isn't complicated: You get a list of clues, and you have to answer each based on the number of boxes allotted for a given answer entry. But as anyone who's ever worked a crossword knows, the answers don't always come easily. Puzzle constructors create crosswords across a wide spectrum of difficulty. The easiest usually have very straightforward clues; the most difficult feature clues that seem downright cryptic. The more creative the puzzle constructor gets with the English language, the greater the challenge you face.

If you're a fan of reading and/or trivia, I suspect you'll enjoy working crosswords. They're a great mental workout; they're as diverse as the English language itself; and even when they frustrate you, they won't bore you. I find there's almost always something new to learn by working a crossword. As long as you give yourself permission to be imperfect — to make mistakes, take guesses, ask a friend for help, and consult outside resources as necessary — you're in for some great fun.

If you're new to working crosswords, keep the following tips in mind.

- ✔ Keep key resources, such as the following, on hand (whether in electronic or hard-copy form):
  - A dictionary
  - A slang dictionary
  - A thesaurus
  - An atlas
  - An almanac

  Some people think that using any resource other than your brain is cheating. But a big part of the fun of working crosswords is learning new stuff, and I'd rather you search for answers in outside resources than simply flip to the answer grid.

- ✔ Work in pencil. When you're an old pro, you may insist on working in pen to up the challenge. But for now, allow for mistakes (which are bound to happen).

✔ Spend some quality time with a puzzle, even if it seems too hard at first. The phrasing of the clues determines each puzzle's difficulty, and it may take a while to get familiar with a puzzle's particular phrasing.

✔ Look for fill-in-the-blank answers first; most people find them among the easiest to solve.

Sudoku

I'd wager that for many people, the appeal of Sudoku is its simplicity. Most often, you're working with a 9-x-9 grid, and your task is to fill in the numbers 1 through 9 one time in each row, column, and 3-x-3 box within the grid. It seems so easy, but the devil is in the puzzle constructor's decisions regarding which numbers to provide. Depending on how many or few numbers are given, and where they appear on the grid, your job may be relatively easy or very, very difficult.

You don't need to know lots of facts or have a big vocabulary to work a Sudoku. But you do need to have a logical mind, lots of patience, and a pencil. (I can almost guarantee you'll do some erasing before settling on final answers.)

If you're ready to join the ranks of Sudoku devotees, keep the following information in mind.

✔ It's harder than it looks! Even with the easiest puzzle, you won't fill in a Sudoku grid in a matter of minutes.

✔ Each puzzle has a unique answer; you can't find multiple ways to solve it.

✔ Start each puzzle by locating obvious, definite answers — those that you can solve simply by looking at what else falls within a particular row, column, and 3-x-3 box.

✔ When you've exhausted the obvious answers, you need to find a systematic way to explore the less-obvious (but still definite) answers.

✔ Myriad advanced strategies exist that aren't covered in this book. If you search for *killer, advanced,* or *extreme Sudoku* online, you'll find countless Web sites that contain strategy suggestions for the toughest of puzzles.

Target Sudoku

If you start getting square eyes from doing regular Sudoku, I can offer some relief in the form of circular Sudoku, sometimes called *target* Sudoku. The target Sudoku is a four-ring circle, as you'll see at the end of Chapter 2. Think of the puzzle as a big pie cut into eight slices, each slice with four bites. Your goal is to place a number into each bite of pie (four numbers to a slice) so that every two adjacent slices contain all of the numbers from 1 to 8. Every ring also must contain all the numbers from 1 to 8.

Here's an important clue: Every other pie slice will contain the same four numbers. That has to be the case because otherwise, you'd have duplicates in some combination of two adjacent slices. However, the four numbers appear in different orders in the different slices because of the fact that each ring comes into play as well.

As with 9-x-9 grid Sudoku puzzles, you start a target Sudoku by trying to identify definite answers: those blank spaces that can have only one answer based on the numbers the puzzle constructor has provided. Target Sudokus are a nice change of pace from regular Sudokus and may be a touch easier because you're dealing with fewer spaces to fill.

Chapter 2

Getting a Puzzle Workout

. . . .

In This Part

▶ Puzzling out logic puzzles and riddles

▶ Getting wordy over word puzzles

▶ Cracking the codes on crossword puzzles

▶ Sinking your teeth into sudoku

. . . .

*P*uzzles are labeled by type and difficulty level. Levels are Easy, Tricky, Tough, and Treacherous, "Easy" being (of course) the easiest puzzles, and "Treacherous" being the most difficult puzzles. When you finish solving all these puzzles, please see Chapter 3 for the answers. Have fun!

Logic Puzzles

Put your thinking cap on to solve these logic puzzles! Each has just one answer.

Tricky

Puzzle 1

A woman gave birth to two boys on the same day, in the same year, within minutes of each other, yet they were not twins. How is this possible?

Puzzle 2

Alexander is a great magician, skilled in many things. He weighs exactly 199 pounds and is about to cross a bridge with a strict weight limit of 200 pounds. The problem is he is carrying three pieces of gold, each weighing 8 ounces each. The gold puts him 8 ounces over the strict weight limit. What did Alexander do to cross the bridge safely with all three pieces of gold?

Tough

Puzzle 3

Two people stand on opposite corners of a handkerchief. They do not stretch or alter the handkerchief in any possible way. How can they both stand on the handkerchief simultaneously without having any possibility whatsoever of touching each other?

Puzzle 4

Under what circumstance could a person walk along a railroad track, discover an oncoming train, and have to run *toward* the train to avoid being struck?

Riddles

Each riddle here has just one answer. Think hard!

Tricky

Puzzle 5

Although it is always before you, what is it you can never see?

Puzzle 6

What goes up and down without actually moving?

Tough

Puzzle 7

What is impossible to hold for more than several minutes although it is lighter than a feather?

Puzzle 8

Homonyms are words that are spelled differently but sound exactly the same. One pair of homonyms is unique in that although they are true homonyms, the two words are also exact opposites of each other. What are the two words?

Cryptograms

Here a phrase or sentence is *encrypted* — each letter is substituted with a different letter or character. To know what the sentence or phrase says, figure out each substitution. Hints are given for each puzzle.

Easy

Puzzle 9

NOWY AJUSYSNN. AC AN COS ZWNC COLC LCCLFOSN
ACNSUR CE COS GENC VZAUUALYC GSCLUN.

Hint: H appears 5 times.

Puzzle 10

UP YIGPBXW QB RQXG FNQXJNFD. FNPR ZIR UPYQZP
AQGOD IF IVR ZQZPVF.

Hint: E appears 6 times.

Tricky

Puzzle 11

WAG MIER CGMCEG OAM ELTWGI WM QMWA TLHGT
MP S PSKLER ZVSXXGE SXG WAG IGFW HMMX IGL-
JAQMXT.

Hint: X appears one time.

Puzzle 12

QCHPHKHN B ZHHV VBFH HMHNUBTBPY, B VBH DXQP
OPWBV WCH ZHHVBPY LGTTHT.

Hint: The letter B is not used at all.

Tough

Puzzle 13

IYUYUSYI, XWYL MWY DYRJTJV ZMIAMZ WEZ ZMAQQ
WY ZWTXZ WEZ SRJVZECY MT WRGQ MWY XTIGC.

Hint: One word ends with O.

Puzzle 14

YDGF A ZAF RGGR ODG DAFSYXQOQOFE CF ODG YANN,
ODGXG QR MXCKAKNP A TDQNS QF ODG HAZQNP.

Hint: The letter U is not used at all.

Treacherous

Puzzle 15

YD AGTTJDY TD HNNHEZCGMMS QDUT ZXH RJYK DN
GMM JZT ADBHQT DN GEZJYV GYK QHGTDYJYV GT
NHGQ.

Hint: U appears just one time.

Puzzle 16

ZNKQYNM OG UPY FKRKFOUM US RYNHSNC RNSRY-
NAM YQYD WPYD GFKNYT PKAH US TYKUP.

Hint: W appears just one time.

Word Scrambles

Unscramble the capitalized word(s) in quotations to
solve the riddles.

Easy

Puzzle 17

How a "RESCUE" can make the saved person feel?

_ _ _ _ _ _

Puzzle 18

What some feel "ELVIS" does? _ _ _ _ _

Puzzle 19

What mishandling "ROSES" can lead to? _ _ _ _ _

24

Tricky

Puzzle 20
While a teacher may be "TEACHING," a student may be? _ _ _ _ _ _ _ _

Puzzle 21
Easy thing to do when one is "SILENT"? _ _ _ _ _ _

Puzzle 22
What "THE EYES" do? _ _ _ _ _ _ _

Puzzle 23
Where a sauce may "THICKEN"? _ _ _ _ _ _ _

Tough

Puzzle 24
Where's a good place to see a "SCHOOL MASTER"? _ _ _ _ _ _ _ _ _ _ _ _

Puzzle 25
What's "TWELVE PLUS ONE"? _ _ _ _ _ _ _ _ _ _ _ _ _

Puzzle 26
What a "BUTTERFLY" may do? _ _ _ _ _ _ _ _ _

Puzzle 27
What "THE DETECTIVES" do?

_ _ _ _ _ _ _ _ _ _ _ _

Treacherous

Puzzle 28
Many people leave "SLOT MACHINES" with? _ _ _ _ _ _
_ _ _ _ _ '

Puzzle 29
What's "HOTTER IN DEGREES"? _ _ _ _ _ _ _ _ _ _ _ _ _
_ _

Puzzle 30
One in a group of "NOTIONS WE RARELY USE"?
_ _ _ _ _ _ _ ' _ _ _ _ _ _ _ _ _ _

Puzzle 31
Payment received? _ _ _ _ _ _ _ _ _ _ _ _ _ _

Word Searches

Try to find as many words as you can in each puzzle.

Tricky

Puzzle 32

CAST	PITCH
CATAPULT	PROJECT
CHUCK	PROPEL
DART	SCATTER
DASH	SEND
EIGHTSIX	SHOOT
EJECT	SLING
FLING	SLOUGH
FLIRT	SPATTER
GETRIDOF	SPREAD
HEAVE	SPRINKLE
HURL	SPURT
JERK	STREW
LAUNCH	THROW
LETFLY	TOSSOUT

```
M Y T E V O W E C P U O Q S F J K F U M X P L
R U Z Y U G E J O H X I S Y T H G I E X Z P R
F G Q S N Z X S D G U Y D W P E X T S S R N U
D O X I N B Y I E W D C H I J A C B T Z G H H
M G L W J F C T V F H A K L J V P R O J E C T
T S L H T H R K I E G P R R V E E E B U X J X
O B Z T B I M O H J W N G T F W T R U P S X V
S F H H D N E S R E T T A C S M S O H N S G X
C I G O Q R E O F C Z G X G S W L E P O R P P
P K F T O S S O U T W B C N T H O W F G I Y V
O A M R E T T A P S G F U I Y I O N S T K W A
C F N G M J P H Q S H M B L P C G O C L P V C
Z J S L U W C M B S U D D F B N A H T X R C V
S S G D Y N I M P E R K D M P E I S S D J D J
X W Q T U L P V R R M A G U C C X L T G A M V
P L T A H O C O I S B U J F B G O Z R E M O B
C O L L M C O T S P O I Z S Y U X B R L S W I
Q H U W K D N U J R G A P X G J H P S O S X V
J L P U R T S P G I C R R H H N S S F G A A H
S Y A Y N T H E L N F H M A Z U M L A J E R K
J J T H R O W Z K K I G M Q E Z I L W D N K H
Z M A N U D S F E L S T N Y P R H G A P I Q V
H O C Q J O J A G E H A T A T Y L F T E L K H
```

Puzzle 33

BABBLE	JABBER
BAWL	NOISE
BELLOW	OUTCRY
BLOWOUT	RACKET
BLUSTER	RIOT
BRATTLE	ROAR
BRAWL	RUMPUS
CLAMOR	SCREECH
CLANGOR	SHOUTING
CLATTER	SHRIEK
CRYING	SQUALLING
DISTURBANCE	STIR
FROLIC	TURBULENCE
FUSS	TURMOIL
HOLLER	UPROAR
HOOTING	WAIL
HOWL	YELL

```
C E T K N C F U L Q B Z I W D F L P M R Y
Y M R H P Q G Z O L X F Q G C U Y N Z S N
U W E I I R R S T A E K X M T S W A O N K
C R T K Z R U R E X P Y O Y Q S N E N X V
G S T C C C N X U G U C P B Q R E B B A J
Y U A L S T N C T G O R O L O N P T E K F
J P L A Q I K S L R N Y X G W O H F W R Q
K M C M Y E A G W A A I F T U A G Z O D E
J U L O I Z N L Y G N N L H V L R L A I Q
G R S R V B Z L R B B G K L L B I B T S E
H F H T O M K A I O J Q O C A C V F O T T
G S L N I Y O B A W L C T R R U S S I U F
K N E T U R B U L E N C E U O C Q K R R C
R B I L O C Y Z H W C T Z C R A L S T B M
B P S T C T H V O E Z E V E E M W D R A E
S L G G U U H L O E W K E N L W O W B N L
G S U F Y O F E T L Y C U O L W O I X C T
E H U S W E H N I B H A B I O K C L L E T
N P W L T C D S N B I R X S H K G I L T A
A C T U L E I G G A Q Y F E L Q E A X E R
G O Z X R J R Q X B Y C V W T U O W O L B
```

Treacherous

Puzzle 34

CALIGINOUS

CLOUDY

DAMP

DARKENED

DREARY

DRIPPY

DRIZZLY

ECLIPSED

FOGGY

GLOOMY

GRAY

HAZY

HEAVY

HUMID

LEADEN

LOWERING

MISTY

MOIST

MOONLESS

MUGGY

MURKY

OBSCURE

OVERCAST

SHADOWY

SOMBER

STARLESS

STEAMY

SUNLESS

UNCLEAR

VAPOROUS

```
E D S L T I I P Z M H S F H E R F Y O I D U Z
G P N S P X I W M H W T H A E C Z Y M A E T S
P M I F J M C R Y A W A O U J A L O G C M Q T
G O M U J U U G G H D B I N D K V I L S L X Y
M H X Q S I R R V A Z V E T W K S Y P A O C U
S J B X X A J I K Z G D R E K J Z N A S W Y H
S Y E T Y F W N C Y A E T I D G Z H F D E Z S
L S F R I H Y T S E B D D D S Z N R D Q R D R
M K E L U U I Y L M N S P F J C M I K W I V Z
J V X L J C L Q O X U P T D E N E K R A D K X
O U A J R Z S S L O V C P K V U W N X E C O J
X R T U Z A X B N Q Z Y I E C D N J K L W N G
J B W I T V T I O D M P Z J B R F C G B O O U
E S R T P M G S W O I E X S V S G E L U O Y L
K D Y R P I D S O V R M U A A S B J E E W W T
Y D U O L C C L Y G N O U P V E E A X N A N S
N Y J A S Y G Y L U R N D H D L Y R D W Y R A
J T C M E G G C N O V R F R K N E W Q M Y L C
K S H T W G C J P P E B I A T O V W O K L C R
B I W E O U P A R A Z P U M Y O M O D D R U E
C M F F C M V S R V P W F X A M Q M C C A W V
X K T K I Y R Y H Y M Y D S S E L N U S L H O
H V A Q T X V H T V J F X Z Z X A T D I V E L S
```

Puzzle 35

ABLAZE	LAMBENT
AFIRE	LUCENT
AFLAME	LUCID
AGLOW	LUMINOUS
ALIGHT	LUSTROUS
BEAM	MAGNIFICENT
BRIGHT	RADIANT
BRILLIANT	RICH
DAZZLE	SHINING
FULGENT	SHINY
GLOSSY	SPLENDID
GORGEOUS	SUNNY
ILLUMINATE	SUPERB
INTENSE	TWINKLING
IRRADIANT	VIVID

```
Q A P C D Z N I H R L A T Q K V I V I D S S Q
Y A F H V J E M R D J A X Q X S T B S U N N Y
C N G I L H Y S S O L G F N Q H X Z Q R U J J
T D L I R R A D I A N T Z Q A D I D N E L P S
X A I U I E G Y T U N O U W C B D F K L E T O
Z Z T M S C Z N I W L R C I O Y L U C I D P A
V Z N H A T E B L N A J O Q G L Y A B Q O M Q
S L E N C G R P R S Y C E I M Y U Z Z S J F O
M E C C L O O O W I C X X L P O I Y B E A I J
L N I U K B L R U W G H E L L A S Q Q P V M W
X Q F Q T F B A G S C H A U O B B N R F J C N
W F I V H G T R M E T P T M W V V R M X P Z E
X W N L G C D F X B O N A I T X I J Z A B A V
F Q G S I B S W F E E U G N K C B D R Y A U R
T N A I L L I R B M V N S A H S U O N I M U L
N X M E A G D E Q A I E T T P H R K Z K Y L K
L J I T S Q N N A L X B N E L G F N T K I K C
M S G T U N S I K F L N G C B R F T G W Z X H
A F U F G B E N N A C S X S E P W E N S N M Y
G D P P U Y I T S I B X Y N I H S I I N Z D L
L V Y X E W T T N K H P A C B Q Y B M H C T A
O R A A T R N H G I X S O L U C E N T O O Q N
W A A L K Y B H Y T N Q Z I D H H R L B E A M
```

Crossword Puzzles

Answer each question based on the number of boxes allotted for a given answer entry.

Easy

Puzzle 36

Across

1. Supergirl's City
5. Balloon
10. Places for pickles
14. Prefix meaning "skin"
15. Shoptalk
16. Words signifying trouble ahead
17. Quickly, quickly
18. Remove a tube top?
19. Joan Sutherland or Judi Dench, e.g.
20. Nobel Peace Prize winner of 1979
23. Have great faith in
24. Grinned from ear to ear
28. Word with Gatos or Altos
29. Really big singer?
32. "___ Sexy" (Right Said Fred tune)
35. Asian peninsula
36. "Well, ___-di-dah"
37. Sounds of pleasure
38. Al Capp's Pansy Yokum
39. Old-time wraparound
40. X-ray supplement
41. Fertile soils
42. Extend a subscription
43. House owner in a Martin Lawrence comedy
45. Lacking brightness
46. Term of respect in colonial India
47. Apollo's twin sister

51. Term of endearment
55. RE:
58. Cheese type
59. Run, but go nowhere
60. Fourth rock from the sun
61. It's for good measure
62. League constituent
63. Capital of Samoa
64. Like a flophouse
65. Sweet potato cousins

Down

1. Sixth U.S. president
2. Plant new crops
3. Frame of bars
4. Belly button
5. Some dust jacket paragraphs
6. Like a dryer's trap, typically
7. Start of many Grimm tales
8. Gelling agent
9. Lift one's spirits?
10. Like the laws of kosher food
11. "Now I get it!"
12. CD follower
13. That boat
21. Ending for switch or buck
22. Overwhelm with humor
25. Bird of prey's weapon
26. Application
27. "Balderdash!"
29. "___ Mia!"

30. Poor contributions?
31. What 5 can represent
32. Frost's feet?
33. Natalie Wood portrayal
34. Chicken portion
35. Title of respect
38. Maternal palindrome
39. Fearlessness
41. The gray wolf
42. "Educating ___" (Caine film)
44. Brunch beverage, perhaps

45. "Once upon a midnight ___
..."
47. Threw in
48. Euripedes tragedy
49. Sunni religion
50. Poppy supporters
52. Leaders in baseball, briefly
53. Pouty look
54. Season to be jolly
55. GPs' grp.
56. Vermont harvest
57. Prefix for pod

Tough

Puzzle 37

Across

1. New Testament book
5. Provide the grub
10. CD followers
14. Marshal Kane's deadline
15. Kicking partner
16. Give off
17. Abandoned queen of Carthage
18. Mechanical learning routines
19. Miami or London, e.g.
20. States dined, except Alaska and Hawaii?
23. Court order
24. Walker on a beat
25. Computer guru
28. Extol
30. Its symbol is an omega
33. Value system
34. Whiskey drink
35. Corn lily
36. Famous warblers making sawbucks?
39. Wine choice
40. Moreover
41. Up until now
42. Burdened beast
43. Units of wire thickness
44. Electorate
45. Big one in London
46. Big rig

47. Last one at the Round Table?
53. Gifted one
54. In the first place?
55. Dynamic start?
57. Top-of-the-line
58. Slowly, to Toscanini
59. Follow
60. Contest
61. Light-show source
62. Sphere's lack

Down

1. Popular joiner
2. Phone cord shape
3. Fuss
4. Gal pal of seven little ones
5. King thriller
6. In the clouds
7. Milosevic predecessor
8. Always
9. Prescription for burnout
10. Go over
11. Leave out
12. Pesky arachnid
13. It's fit for a pig
21. "Love Story" author Segal
22. Hebrew letter
25. One more than tri-
26. Morals standards
27. Fischer's game
28. Rich soil
29. Camera setting
30. Type of daisy
31. Human Resources person, at times

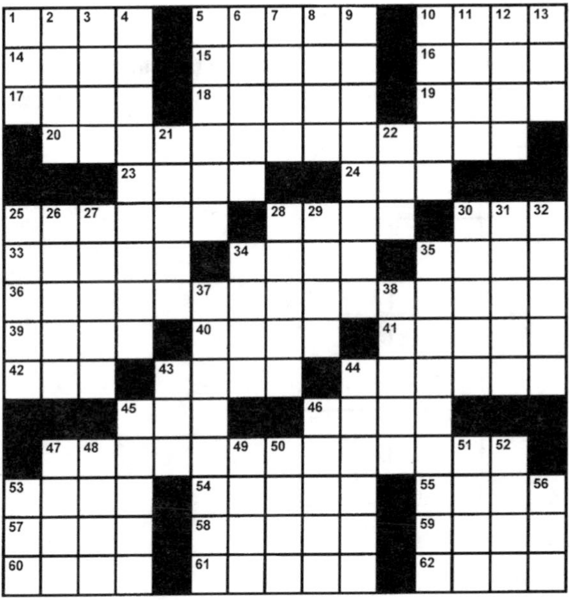

(crossword grid)

32. Sails' staffs
34. Order to a broker
35. Be behind
37. Precipitation type
38. David's great-grandmother
43. Blanc or Torme
44. Merchant
45. Jewel holder
46. An old one may need a key

47. Commandment word
48. Sparkling, for one
49. "Take ___ Train" (Duke Ellington)
50. Feathered females
51. Kind of hunter
52. Math subj.
53. Roll for a high roller
56. Seville cheer

Sudoku Puzzles

Fill in the numbers 1 through 9 one time in each row, column, and 3-x-3 box within the grid.

Tricky

Puzzle 38

			4			1		9
4			7			5	8	2
	2		6		9	8	7	
5								3
	1	9	3		5		2	
1	6	5			8			7
8		3			7			

Tough

Puzzle 39

	4		1					
5	2							
		6		5		7		
2			3	1			5	
		3	9		2	6		
	1			8	7			2
		8		3		9		
							6	3
				9			7	

Target Sudoku Puzzles

Place a number into each section so every two adjacent slices and every ring contain the numbers 1 through 8.

Easy
Puzzle 40

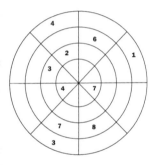

Tricky
Puzzle 41

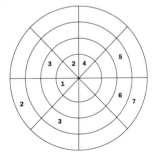

Tough
Puzzle 42

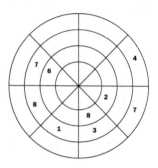

Chapter 3

Checking Your Answers

• •

*P*lease do not read through this part until you've worked on the puzzles in Chapter 2!

Logic Puzzle Answers

Tricky

Puzzle 1
They were part of a set of triplets, the third child being a daughter

Puzzle 2
Alexander juggled the gold as he crossed the bridge, keeping at least one piece in the air at all times.

Tough

Puzzle 3
One person stands on one corner of the handkerchief and closes a door. The second person stands on the corner of the handkerchief protruding under the door. With the door between them, they cannot possibly touch.

Puzzle 4

The person is on tracks in a railroad tunnel walking toward the train and is close to the end when the oncoming train is discovered. The person must then run forward to clear the tunnel before the train enters.

Riddle Answers

Tricky

Puzzle 5

The future

Puzzle 6

Stairs

Tough

Puzzle 7

Your breath

Puzzle 8

Raise and raze

Cryptogram Answers

Easy

Puzzle 9

SHUN IDLENESS. IT IS THE RUST THAT ATTACHES ITSELF TO THE MOST BRILLIANT METALS.

Puzzle 10

BE CAREFUL OF YOUR THOUGHTS. THEY MAY
BECOME WORDS AT ANY MOMENT.

Tricky

Puzzle 11

THE ONLY PEOPLE WHO LISTEN TO BOTH SIDES OF A
FAMILY QUARREL ARE THE NEXT DOOR NEIGHBORS.

Puzzle 12

WHENEVER I FEEL LIKE EXERCISING, I LIE DOWN
UNTIL THE FEELING PASSES.

Tough

Puzzle 13

REMEMBER, WHEN THE PEACOCK STRUTS HIS STUFF
HE SHOWS HIS BACKSIDE TO HALF THE WORLD.

Puzzle 14

WHEN A MAN SEES THE HANDWRITING ON THE WALL,
THERE IS PROBABLY A CHILD IN THE FAMILY.

Treacherous

Puzzle 15

NO PASSION SO EFFECTUALLY ROBS THE MIND OF ALL
ITS POWERS OF ACTING AND REASONING AS FEAR.

Puzzle 16

BRAVERY IS THE CAPACITY TO PERFORM PROPERLY
EVEN WHEN SCARED HALF TO DEATH.

Word Scramble Answers

Easy

Puzzle 17
SECURE

Puzzle 18
LIVES

Puzzle 19
SORES

Tricky

Puzzle 20
CHEATING

Puzzle 21
LISTEN

Puzzle 22
THEY SEE

Puzzle 23
KITCHEN

Tough

Puzzle 24
THE CLASSROOM

Word Search Answers

Tricky

Puzzle 32

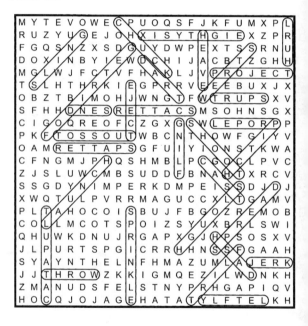

Puzzle 33

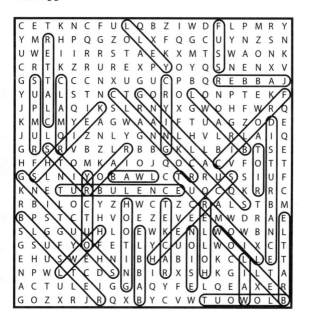

Treacherous

Puzzle 34

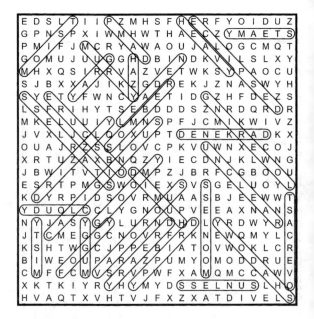

Puzzle 35

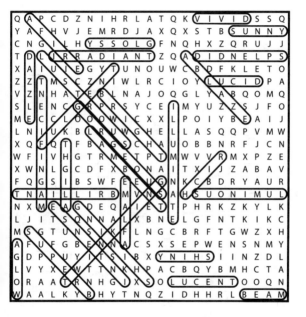

Crossword Answers
Easy
Puzzle 36

¹A	²R	³G	⁴O		⁵B	⁶L	⁷O	⁸A	⁹T		¹⁰J	¹¹A	¹²R	¹³S

The grid reads:

- ¹A ²R ³G ⁴O — ⁵B ⁶L ⁷O ⁸A ⁹T — ¹⁰J ¹¹A ¹²R ¹³S
- ¹⁴D E R M — ¹⁵L I N G O — ¹⁶U H O H
- ¹⁷A S A P — ¹⁸U N C A P — ¹⁹D A M E
- ²⁰M O T H ²¹E R T E R E ²²S A
- ²³S W E A R B Y — ²⁴L I ²⁵T ²⁶U ²⁷P
- ²⁸L O S — ²⁹M ³⁰A ³¹M A C A S S
- ³²I M ³³T ³⁴O O — ³⁵M A L A Y — ³⁶L A H
- ³⁷A A H S — ³⁸M A M M Y — ³⁹T O G A
- ⁴⁰M R I — ⁴¹L O A M S — ⁴²R E N E W
- ⁴³B I G ⁴⁴M O M M A — ⁴⁵D I M
- ⁴⁶S A H I B — ⁴⁷A R T E ⁴⁸M ⁴⁹I ⁵⁰S
- ⁵¹M O ⁵²M ⁵³M ⁵⁴Y D E A R E S T
- ⁵⁵A ⁵⁶S ⁵⁷T O — ⁵⁸G O U D A — ⁵⁹I D L E
- ⁶⁰M A R S — ⁶¹R U L E R — ⁶²T E A M
- ⁶³A P I A — ⁶⁴S E E D Y — ⁶⁵Y A M S

Tough

Puzzle 37

A¹	C²	T³	S⁴		C⁵	A⁶	T⁷	E⁸	R⁹		R¹⁰	O¹¹	M¹²	S¹³
N¹⁴	O	O	N		A¹⁵	L	I	V	E		E¹⁶	M	I	T
D¹⁷	I	D	O		R¹⁸	O	T	E	S		C¹⁹	I	T	Y
	L²⁰	O	W	E²¹	R	F	O	R	T	Y²²	A	T	E	
		W²³	R	I	T			C²⁴	O	P				
T²⁵	E²⁶	C²⁷	H	I	E		L²⁸	A²⁹	U	D		O³⁰	H³¹	M³²
E³³	T	H	I	C		S³⁴	O	U	R		I³⁵	X	I	A
T³⁶	H	E	T	H³⁷	R	E	E	T	E	N³⁸	N	E	R	S
R³⁹	O	S	E		A⁴⁰	L	S	O		A⁴¹	S	Y	E	T
A⁴²	S	S		M⁴³	I	L	S		V⁴⁴	O	T	E	R	S
			B⁴⁵	E	N		S⁴⁶	E	M	I				
	T⁴⁷	W⁴⁸	E	L	F	T⁴⁹	H⁵⁰	K	N	I	G	H⁵¹	T⁵²	
W⁵³	H	I	Z		A⁵⁴	H	E	A	D		A⁵⁵	E	R	O⁵⁶
A⁵⁷	O	N	E		L⁵⁸	E	N	T	O		T⁵⁹	A	I	L
D⁶⁰	U	E	L		L⁶¹	A	S	E	R		E⁶²	D	G	E

Sudoku Answers

Tricky

Puzzle 38

6	7	8	4	5	2	1	3	9
9	5	2	8	3	1	7	6	4
4	3	1	7	9	6	5	8	2
3	2	4	6	1	9	8	7	5
5	8	6	2	7	4	9	1	3
7	1	9	3	8	5	4	2	6
1	6	5	9	2	8	3	4	7
2	9	7	1	4	3	6	5	8
8	4	3	5	6	7	2	9	1

Tough

Puzzle 39

9	4	7	1	6	8	2	3	5
5	2	1	7	9	3	8	4	6
8	3	6	2	5	4	7	1	9
2	8	9	3	1	6	4	5	7
7	5	3	9	4	2	6	8	1
6	1	4	5	8	7	3	9	2
1	7	8	6	3	5	9	2	4
4	9	2	8	7	1	5	6	3
3	6	5	4	2	9	1	7	8